4-Cho Songbook
Classic Hits

WISE PUBLICATIONS
part of The Music Sales Group
London / New York / Paris / Sydney / Copenhagen / Berlin / Madrid / Tokyo

This *4-Chord Songbook* allows even beginner guitarists to play and enjoy classic hits. With the same 4 chords used throughout the book, you'll soon master your favourite hits and classic songs.

The *4-Chord Songbook* doesn't use music notation. Throughout the book chord boxes are printed at the head of each song; the chord changes are shown above the lyrics. It's left to you, the guitarist, to decide on a strum pattern or picking pattern.

You might find that the pitch of the vocal line is not always comfortable because it is pitched too high or too low. In that case, you can change the key without learning a new set of chords; simply place a capo behind a suitable fret.

Whatever you do, this *4-Chord Songbook* guarantees hours of enjoyment for guitarists of all levels, as well as providing a fine basis for building a strong repertoire.

Published by
Wise Publications
14-15 Berners Street, London W1T 3LJ, UK.

Exclusive Distributors:
Music Sales Limited
Distribution Centre, Newmarket Road, Bury St Edmunds, Suffolk IP33 3YB, UK.
Music Sales Pty Limited
20 Resolution Drive, Caringbah, NSW 2229, Australia.

Order No. AM987767
ISBN 1-84609-775-4
This book © Copyright 2006 Wise Publications,
a division of Music Sales Limited.

Printed in the EU.

www.musicsales.com

Your Guarantee of Quality

As publishers, we strive to produce every book to the highest commercial standards.

The music has been freshly engraved and the book has been carefully designed to minimise awkward page turns and to make playing from it a real pleasure.

Particular care has been given to specifying acid-free, neutral-sized paper made from pulps which have not been elemental chlorine bleached.

This pulp is from farmed sustainable forests and was produced with special regard for the environment.

Throughout, the printing and binding have been planned to ensure a sturdy, attractive publication which should give years of enjoyment.

If your copy fails to meet our high standards, please inform us and we will gladly replace it.

elative Tuning

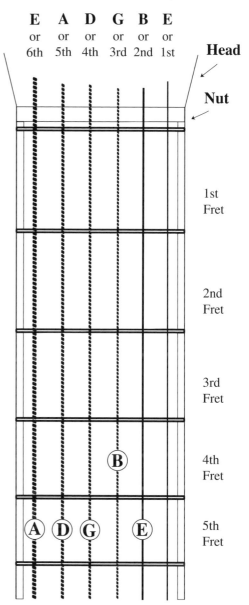

he guitar can be tuned with the aid of pitch pes or dedicated electronic guitar tuners hich are available through your local music ealer. If you do not have a tuning device, ou can use relative tuning. Estimate the tch of the 6th string as near as possible to or at least a comfortable pitch (not too gh, as you might break other strings in ning up). Then, while checking the various ositions on the diagram, place a finger from our left hand on the:

h fret of the E or 6th string and **tune the** en A (or 5th string) to the note (A)

h fret of the A or 5th string and **tune the** en D (or 4th string) to the note (D)

h fret of the D or 4th string and **tune the** en G (or 3rd string) to the note (G)

h fret of the G or 3rd string and **tune the** en B (or 2nd string) to the note (B)

h fret of the B or 2nd string and **tune the** en E (or 1st string) to the note (E)

eading Chord Boxes

hord boxes are diagrams of the guitar neck viewed head upwards, face on as lustrated. The top horizontal line is the nut, unless a higher fret number is indicated, e others are the frets.

he vertical lines are the strings, starting from E (or 6th) 1 the left to E (or 1st) on the right.

he black dots indicate where to place your fingers.

rings marked with an O are played open, not fretted.
rings marked with an X should not be played.

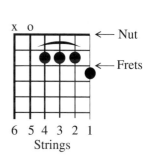

3

All Along The Watchtower

Words & Music by
Bob Dylan

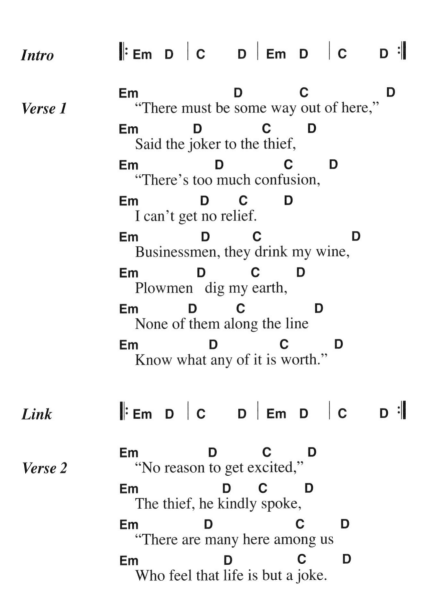

Intro

‖: Em D | C   D | Em D | C   D :‖

Verse 1

Em   D   C   D
"There must be some way out of here,"

Em   D   C   D
Said the joker to the thief,

Em   D   C   D
"There's too much confusion,

Em   D C   D
I can't get no relief.

Em   D   C   D
Businessmen, they drink my wine,

Em   D   C   D
Plowmen   dig my earth,

Em   D   C   D
None of them along the line

Em   D   C   D
Know what any of it is worth."

Link

‖: Em D | C   D | Em D | C   D :‖

Verse 2

Em   D   C D
"No reason to get excited,"

Em   D C   D
The thief, he kindly spoke,

Em   D   C   D
"There are many here among us

Em   D   C   D
Who feel that life is but a joke.

ont.

```
Em              D        C                    D
    But you and I, we've been through that,
Em              D        C    D
    And this is not our fate,
Em              D        C                D
    So let us not talk falsely now,
Em              D          C    D
    The hour is getting late."
```

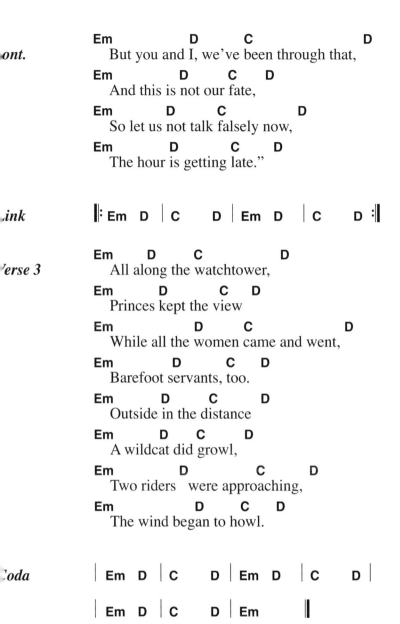

Link

```
‖: Em  D  | C      D | Em  D  | C      D :‖
```

Verse 3

```
Em          D        C                D
    All along the watchtower,
Em          D          C    D
    Princes kept the view
Em                  D        C                D
    While all the women came and went,
Em          D        C    D
    Barefoot servants, too.
Em          D        C        D
    Outside in the distance
Em          D        C        D
    A wildcat did growl,
Em                  D              C        D
    Two riders   were approaching,
Em                  D        C    D
    The wind began to howl.
```

Coda

```
| Em  D  | C      D | Em  D  | C      D |

| Em  D  | C      D | Em        ‖
```

Candle In The Wind

Words & Music by
Elton John & Bernie Taupin

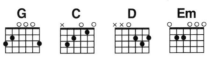

Intro | G C G C | G D ‖

Verse 1

G
Goodbye Norma Jean,

               C
Though I never   knew you at all

               G
You had the grace to hold yourself,

               C
While those around you crawled.

               G
They crawled out of the woodwork,

               C
And they whispered   into your brain,

               G
They set you on the treadmill

               C
And they made you change your name.

Chorus 1

        D
And it seems to me you lived your life

  G   **C**
Like a candle in the wind,

  G
Never knowing who to cling to

      D
When the rain set in.

    C
And I would have liked to have known you,

        Em
But I was just a kid,

             D
Your candle burned out long before

    C   **G C**
Your legend ever did.

Link 1 | G | D C G C | G D ‖

                         G
Verse 2   Loneliness was tough,
                                 C
                 The toughest role   you ever played.
                                      G
                 Hollywood created a superstar,
                                          C
                 And pain was the price you paid.
                              G
                 Even when you died,
                          C
                 Oh the press still hounded you,
                              G
                 All the papers had to say
                                      C
                 Was that Marilyn was found in the nude.

Chorus 2   As Chorus 1

Link 2   As Link 1

                         G
Verse 3   Goodbye Norma Jean,
                             C
                 Though I never   knew you at all
                                      G
                 You had the grace to hold yourself,
                                          C
                 While those around you crawled.
                 G
                 Goodbye Norma Jean,
                                      C
                 From the young man in the 22nd row
                                      G
                 Who sees you as something more than sexual,
                                  C
                 More than just our Marilyn Monroe.

Chorus 3   As Chorus 1

                         G   D
Outro   Your candle burned out long before
                          C   G C G
                 Your legend ever did.

Crash

Words & Music by
Paul Court, Stephen Dullaghan & Tracy Spencer

G   C   D

Intro   ‖: G | G | D | C   :‖

Verse 1
       N.C   G   C
Here you go, way too fast,
       D   C
Don't slow down you're gonna crash,
                G   C
You should watch, watch your step,
       D   C
If you don't look out, you're gonna break your neck.
         G   C
So shut, shut your mouth
           D   C
'Cos I'm not listening anyhow.
          G   C
I've had e - nough, enough of you
         D   C
E - nough to last a lifetime through.
         D
So what do you want of me?
G   C
Got no words of sympathy,
        D   C
And if I go around with you,
        G   C   D | D
You know that I've been messed up too, with you.

Interlude
G   C   D   C
Na, na, na, na, na, na, na, na, na, na, na,
G   C   D   C
Na, na, na, na, na, na, na, na, na, na, na.

Verse 2

```
N.C        G              C
Here you go, way too fast,
D                          C
Don't slow down you're gonna crash,
          G              C
You don't know what's been going down,
D                        C
You've been running all over town.
    G  N.C      C
So shut, shut your mouth       G
      D            C
'Cos I'm not listening anyhow.
         G              C
I've had enough, enough of you
      D            C
E - nough to last a lifetime through.
      D
So what do you want of me?
G              C
Got no cure for misery,
        D              C
And if I go around with you,
    G              C          D  │ D    │
You know that I've been messed up too, with you.
```

Interlude

```
          D
‖: With you, with you.
G        C              D
Na, na, na, na, na, na, na, na, na, na, na,
                    C
(Slow down you're gonna crash)
G        C              D
Na, na, na, na, na, na, na, na, na, na, na.
                    C
(Slow down you're gonna crash)  :‖
```

Repeat to fade

Cream

Words & Music by
Prince

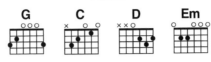

Intro   4 bars drums   ‖: G | C | G | G   :‖

Verse 1

```
     G
   This is it,
     C                   G
It's time for u to go to the wire.

U will hit,
     C                   G
Cuz u got the burnin' desire.

It's your time, (Time)
     C                        G
U got the horn so why don't u blow it.

U are fine, (Fine)
        C                      G
U're filthy cute and baby u know it.
```

Chorus 1

```
   G       D
Cream, get on top,
   G       D
Cream, u will cop,
   G       D
Cream, don't u stop
   C       Em    G
Cream, sh-boogie bop.
```

Verse 2

```
            G
U're so good,
   C                        G
Baby there ain't nobody better (Ain't nobody better).

So u should
```

        C   G
Never, ever go by the letter. (Never ever)

U're so cool, (Cool)
      C   G
Everything u do is success.

Make the rules, (Rules)
             C
Then break them all cuz u are the best.

Yes u are.

Chorus 2   As Chorus 1

        N.C.
Look up in the air, it's your tower.

Instrumental | G | G | G | C | G |

        G
Verse 3   Do your dance,
      C   G
Why should u wait any longer?

Take your chance,
      C   G
It could only make u stronger.

It's your time, (Time)
        C   G
U got the horn so why don't u blow it.

U're so fine, (Fine)
         C   G
U're filthy cute and baby u know it.

Chorus 3   As Chorus 1

N.C.
Cream, cream.
C   Em   G
Cream, sh-boogie bop.

Chorus 4   ‖: As Chorus 1 w/ad lib vocals :‖   *Repeat to fade*

"Heroes"

Words by David Bowie
Music by David Bowie and Brian Eno

G   C   D   Em

Intro

‖: D | D | G | G :‖

Verse 1

D   G   D   G
I, I will be king, and you, you will be queen.

            C   D
Though nothing, will drive them away

           C   Em   D
We can beat them,   just for one day.

           C   G   D
We can be heroes, just for one day.

                            G
And you, you can be mean.

          D   G
And I, I'll drink all the time

                 D   G
'Cause we're lovers, and that is a fact.

                D   G
Yes we're lovers, and that is that.

           C   D
Though nothing, will keep us together

              C   Em   D
We could steal time,   just for one day.

           C   G   D
We can be heroes,   for ever and ever. What d'you say?

Link 1

‖: D | D | G | G :‖

Verse 2

D   G
I, I wish you could swim

          D   G
Like the dolphins, like dolphins can swim.

          C   D
Though nothing, nothing will keep us together,

          C   Em   D
We can beat them,   for ever and ever

           C   G   D
Oh we can be heroes, just for one day.

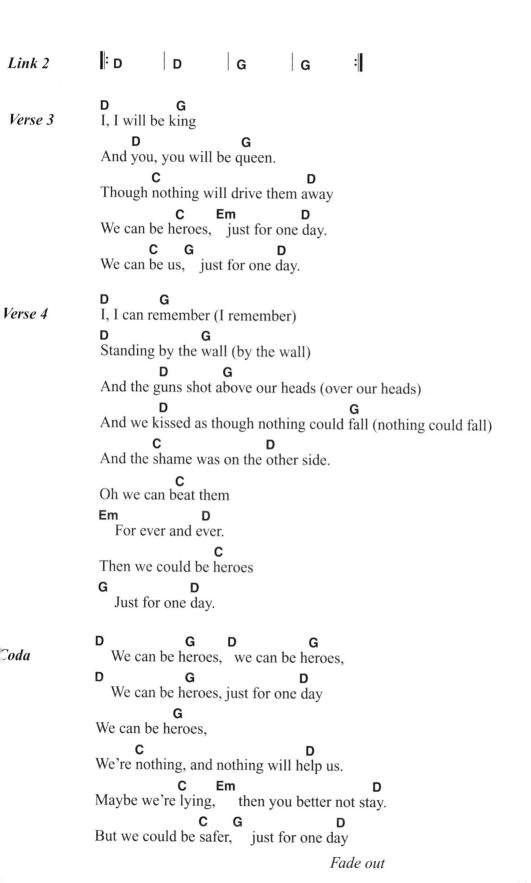

Link 2   ‖: D | D | G | G   :‖

Verse 3
```
     D          G
I, I will be king
        D              G
And you, you will be queen.
          C                    D
Though nothing will drive them away
            C     Em         D
We can be heroes,   just for one day.
            C   G          D
We can be us,  just for one day.
```

Verse 4
```
     D        G
I, I can remember (I remember)
D                    G
Standing by the wall (by the wall)
          D          G
And the guns shot above our heads (over our heads)
            D                         G
And we kissed as though nothing could fall (nothing could fall)
            C              D
And the shame was on the other side.
               C
Oh we can beat them
Em            D
   For ever and ever.
                 C
Then we could be heroes
G            D
   Just for one day.
```

Coda
```
D              G     D          G
   We can be heroes,   we can be heroes,
D              G            D
   We can be heroes, just for one day
               G
We can be heroes,
       C                       D
We're nothing, and nothing will help us.
            C     Em                 D
Maybe we're lying,    then you better not stay.
                C   G            D
But we could be safer,   just for one day
```
                                    Fade out

I'm A Believer

Words & Music by
Neil Diamond

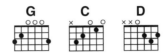

Intro

| G   C | D | D ||

Verse 1

G   D   G
I thought love was only true in fairy tales,

                     D   G
Meant for someone else but not for me.

C   G   C
Love was out to get me (da da da da da),

                  G   C
That's the way it seems (da da da da da),

                   G   D
Disappointment haunted all my dreams.

Chorus 1

N.C.   G   C G   C   G   C G
Then I saw her face,   now I'm a believer.

C   G   C G   C   G   C G
Not a trace   of doubt in my mind,

C   G N.C. C   G
I'm in love,   oh, I'm a believer,

               C   D
I couldn't leave her if I tried.

Verse 2

G   D   G
I thought love was more or less a given thing,

                     D   G
It seems the more I gave the less I got.

C   G   C
What's the use in trying (da da da da da),

                  G   C
All you get is pain (da da da da da),

                   G   D
When I needed sunshine I got rain.

Chorus 2

N.C.   G   C G   C   G   C G
Then I saw her face,   now I'm a believer.

C   G   C G C   G   C G
Not a trace   of doubt in my mind,

C   G N.C. C   G
I'm in love,   oh, I'm a believer,

             C   D
I couldn't leave her if I tried.

Solo

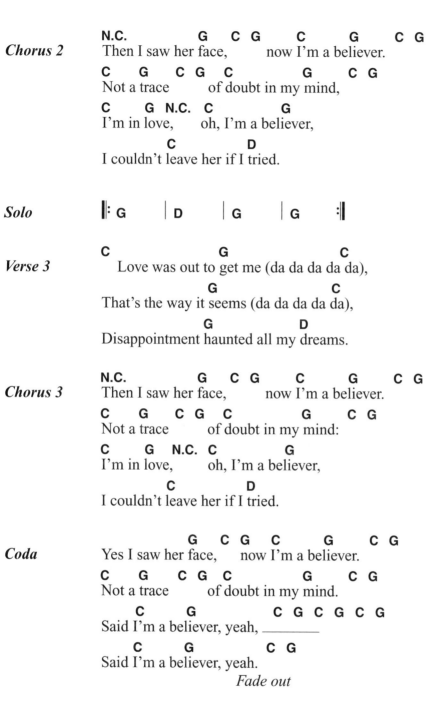

‖: G | D | G | G   :‖

Verse 3

C   G   C
   Love was out to get me (da da da da da),

            G   C
That's the way it seems (da da da da da),

            G   D
Disappointment haunted all my dreams.

Chorus 3

N.C.   G   C G   C   G   C G
Then I saw her face,   now I'm a believer.

C   G   C G C   G   C G
Not a trace   of doubt in my mind:

C   G N.C. C   G
I'm in love,   oh, I'm a believer,

             C   D
I couldn't leave her if I tried.

Coda

                G   C G   C   G   C G
Yes I saw her face,   now I'm a believer.

C   G   C G C   G   C G
Not a trace   of doubt in my mind.

      C   G   C G C G C G
Said I'm a believer, yeah, ⎯⎯⎯

      C   G   C G
Said I'm a believer, yeah.
                Fade out

Livin' On A Prayer

Words & Music by
Richie Sambora, Desmond Child & Jon Bon Jovi

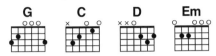

Verse 1

Em
Tommy used to work on the docks,

                                             C   **D**
Union's been on strike, he's down on his luck, it's tough,

Em
So tough.

Gina works the diner all day,

                                       C   **D**
Working for her man, she brings home her pay for love,

Em
For love.

Bridge 1

                            C   **D**   **Em**
She says we've got to hold on to what we've got,

     C   **D**   **Em**
It doesn't make a difference if we make it or not,

        C   **D**   **Em** **C**
We've got each other and that's a lot for love,

       D
We'll give it a shot.

Chorus 1

Em C   **D**
Oh,   we're half way there,

G C D
Oh,   livin' on a prayer,

Em   **C**   **D**
Take my hand, we'll make it I swear,

G C D   **Em**
Oh,   livin' on a prayer.

Verse 2

Em
Tommy got his six-string in hock,

                                                        C   D
Now he's holding in when he used to make it talk so tough,

    Em
It's tough.

Gina dreams of running away,

                                                 C   D
When she cries in the night Tommy whispers "Baby, it's o.k."

      Em
Some day.

Bridge 2   As Bridge 1

Chorus 2

Em C   D
Oh,   we're half way there,

G C D
Oh,   livin' on a prayer,

Em   C   D
Take my hand, we'll make it I swear,

G C D
Oh,   livin' on a prayer,

C
Livin' on a prayer.

Guitar solo | Em C | D | G   C | D |

                      | Em C | D | G   C | Em |

Em   C   D   Em
We've got to hold on, ready or not,

        C   D
You live for the fight when that's all you've got.

Chorus 3   As Chorus 1 *(Ad lib. to fade)*

One Love/People Get Ready

Words & Music by
Bob Marley & Curtis Mayfield

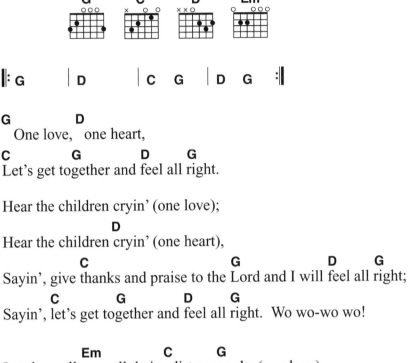

Intro ‖: G │ D │ C G │ D G :‖

Chorus 1

    G   **D**
  One love, one heart,
C   **G**   **D**   **G**
Let's get together and feel all right.

Hear the children cryin' (one love);
                D
Hear the children cryin' (one heart),
          C   **G**   **D** **G**
Sayin', give thanks and praise to the Lord and I will feel all right;
         C   **G**   **D**   **G**
Sayin', let's get together and feel all right. Wo wo-wo wo!

Verse 1

            Em   **C**   **G**
Let them all pass all their dirty remarks (one love),
            Em   **C** **D** **G**
There is one question I'd really love to ask (one heart!),
        Em   **C**   **G**
Is there a place for the hopeless sinner,
                  Em   **C** **D** **G**
Who has hurt all mankind just to save his   own beliefs?

Chorus 2

                        D
One love, what about the one heart? One heart,
        C   **G**   **D**   **G**
What about? Let's get together and feel all right.

As it was in the beginning (one love),
                D
So shall it be in the end (one heart),

All right!

cont.

     C   G   D   G
Give thanks and praise to the Lord and I will feel all right,
C   G   D   G
Let's get together and feel all right.

One more thing!

Verse 2

                 Em   C   G
Let's get together to fight this Holy Armagiddyon (one love),
                Em   C   D   G
So when the Man comes there will   be no, no doom (one song).
                 Em   C   G
Have pity on those whose chances grows t'inner;
                  Em   C   D   G
There ain't no hiding place from the Father of Creation.

Chorus 3

                                    D
Sayin' one love, what about the one heart? (one heart),

What about the...
C   G   D   G
Let's get together and feel all right.

I'm pleadin' to mankind! (one love),
       D
Oh, Lord! (One heart.) Wo-ooh!
     C   G   D   G
Give thanks and praise to the Lord and I will feel all right,
C   G   D   G
Let's get together and feel all right.
     C   G   D   G
Give thanks and praise to the Lord and I will feel all right,
C   G   D   G
Let's get together and feel all right.   *Fade out*

No Woman, No Cry

Words & Music by
Vincent Ford

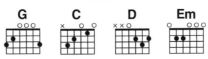

Intro   ‖: G D │ Em C │ G C │ G D :‖ *Play 4 times*

Chorus 1
G   D   Em C
No woman, no cry,
G   C   G   D
No woman, no cry,
G   D   Em C
No woman, no cry,
G   C   G   D
No woman, no cry.

Verse 1
G   C   D   Em   C
Say, say,   said I remember when we used to sit
G   D   Em   C
In the government yard in Trenchtown,
G   D   Em   C
Oba-observing the hypocrites
            G   D   Em   C
As they   would mingle with the good people we meet.
G   D   Em   C
Good friends we have had, oh good friends we've lost
G   D   Em   C
Along the way.
G   D   Em   C
In this bright future you can't forget your past,
G   D   Em   C
So dry your tears, I say,   and

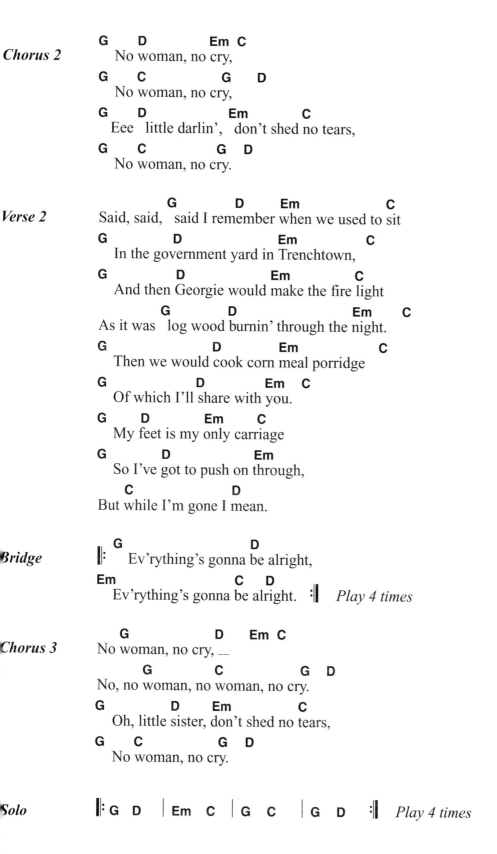

Chorus 2

G   D   Em C
   No woman, no cry,

G   C   G   D
   No woman, no cry,

G   D   Em   C
   Eee little darlin',   don't shed no tears,

G   C   G   D
   No woman, no cry.

Verse 2

            G   D   Em   C
Said, said,   said I remember when we used to sit

G   D   Em   C
   In the government yard in Trenchtown,

G   D   Em   C
   And then Georgie would make the fire light

            G   D   Em C
As it was   log wood burnin' through the night.

G   D   Em   C
   Then we would cook corn meal porridge

G   D   Em C
   Of which I'll share with you.

G   D   Em   C
   My feet is my only carriage

G   D   Em
   So I've got to push on through,

    C   D
But while I'm gone I mean.

Bridge

    G   D
𝄆:   Ev'rything's gonna be alright,

Em   C   D
   Ev'rything's gonna be alright. :𝄇 *Play 4 times*

Chorus 3

         G   D   Em C
No woman, no cry, —

           G   C   G   D
No, no woman, no woman, no cry.

G   D   Em   C
   Oh, little sister, don't shed no tears,

G   C   G   D
   No woman, no cry.

Solo

𝄆: G D | Em C | G C | G D :𝄇 *Play 4 times*

Verse 3

```
             G          D      Em             C
Said, said,  said I remember when we used to sit
     G            D            Em           C
In the government yard in Trenchtown,
     G            D            Em           C
And then Georgie would make the fire light
              G           D             Em       C
As it was   log wood burnin' through the night.
     G                 D         Em          C
Then we would cook corn meal porridge
     G              D        Em   C
Of which I'll share with you.
     G     D      Em      C
My feet is my only carriage
     G        D           Em
So I've got to push on through,
          C             D
But while I'm gone I mean.
```

Chorus 4

```
     G    D          Em  C
No woman, no cry,
     G    C          G   D
No woman, no cry,
     G              D        Em            C
Oh c'mon little darlin', say don't shed no tears,
     G    C          G  D
No woman, no cry,   yeah!
```

Chorus 5

```
     G       D      Em            C
(Little darlin', don't shed no tears,
     G    C          G   D
No woman, no cry.
     G       C    G
Little sister, don't shed no tears,
         C          G   D
No woman, no cry.)
```

Coda

```
| G  D   | Em  C  | G  C  | G  D  |

| G  D   | Em  C  | G  C  | G     ||
```

22

Romeo And Juliet

Words & Music by
Mark Knopfler

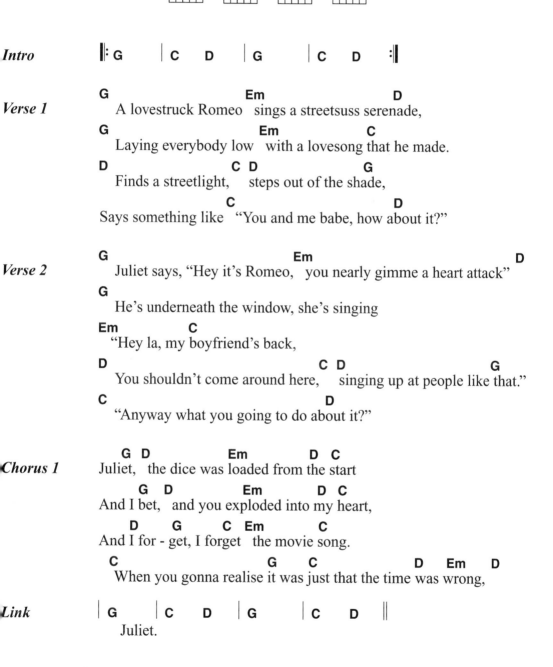

Intro

|: G | C D | G | C D :|

Verse 1

G   Em   D
A lovestruck Romeo   sings a streetsuss serenade,

G   Em   C
Laying everybody low   with a lovesong that he made.

D   C D   G
Finds a streetlight,   steps out of the shade,

                    C   D
Says something like   "You and me babe, how about it?"

Verse 2

G   Em   D
Juliet says, "Hey it's Romeo,   you nearly gimme a heart attack"

G
He's underneath the window, she's singing

Em   C
"Hey la, my boyfriend's back,

D   C D   G
You shouldn't come around here,   singing up at people like that."

C   D
"Anyway what you going to do about it?"

Chorus 1

         G D   Em   D C
Juliet,   the dice was loaded from the start

         G D   Em   D C
And I bet,   and you exploded into my heart,

         D   G   C Em   C
And I for - get, I forget   the movie song.

         C   G   C   D Em   D
When you gonna realise it was just that the time was wrong,

Link

| G | C D | G | C D ||

Juliet.

Verse 3

```
        G                          Em                              D
        Come up on different streets,   they both were streets of shame,
        G                      Em                  C
        Both dirty, both mean,   yes and the dream was just the same.
        D                              C     D              G
        And I dreamed your dream for you   and now your dream is real.
        C                                    D
        How can you look at me as if I was just another one of your deals?
```

Verse 4

```
                      G                    D
        When you can fall for chains of silver,
        Em                               D
        You can fall for chains of gold,
        G                          Em            C          D
        You can fall for pretty strangers     and the promises they hold.
                          C   D              G
        You promised me everything,       you promised me thick and thin,
        C
        Now you just say, "Oh Romeo, yeah, you know,
          D
        I used to have a scene with him."
```

Chorus 2

```
          G   D              Em            D C
        Juliet,   when we made love you used to cry.
                  G              D              Em       D C
        You said "I love you like the stars above, I'll love you till I die."
        D       G      C  Em                      C
        There's a place for us,     you know the movie song,
          C                      G     C              D     Em    D
          When you gonna realise it was just that the time was wrong,

        Juli-(et.)
```

Link

```
        ‖ G     ‖ C   D  ‖ G     ‖ C   D  ‖
        -et
```

Verse 5

```
        G                  Em                      D
        I can't do the talk     like they talk on TV,
        G                      Em                  C
        And I can't do a love song     like the way it's meant to be,
        D                  C     D              G
        I can't do everything but I'd do anything for you,
        C                          D
        I can't do anything except be in love with you.
```

Verse 6

```
       G                         Em                      D
       And all I do is miss you     and the way we used to be,
       G                         Em          C
       All I do is keep the beat     and bad company,
       D                  C
       All I do is kiss you
       D                       G
       Through the bars of a rhyme.
       C                              D
       Julie, I'd do the stars with you   any time.
```

Chorus 3

```
          G   D              Em           D C
       Juliet,   when we made love you used to cry.
                  G              D           Em       D C
       You said "I love you like the stars above, I'll love you till I die."
       D        G     D  C  Em              C
       There's a place for us,     you know the movie song,
       C                          G   C          D   Em    D
         When you gonna realise it was just that the time was wrong,

       Ju(-u-u-liet.)
```

Link

```
    | G       | C    D  | G       | C    D  |
       -u-u-liet.

    | G       | C    D  | G       | C    D  ||
```

Verse 7

```
       G                       Em                     D
       And a lovestruck Romeo     sings a streetsuss serenade,
       G                     Em            C
       Laying everybody low     with a lovesong that he made.
       D                  C
       Finds a convenient streetlight,
       D              G
       Steps out of the shade,
                      C                  D
       Says something like  "You and me babe,     how about it?"
```

Coda

```
    ||: C      | D      | C      | D      :||   Repeat ad lib. to fade
```

Sit Down

Words & Music by
Tim Booth, Larry Gott, Jim Glennie & Gavan Whelan

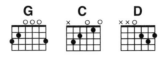

Intro ‖: G | G | C | D   :‖

Verse 1

G   C   D
I'll sing myself to sleep, a song from the darkest hour.
G   C   D
Secret's I can't keep inside all the day.
G   C   D
Swing from high to deep, extremes of sweet and sour.
G   C D
Hope that God exists, I hope, I pray.

Bridge

G
Drawn by the undertow,
   C   D
My life is out of control.
G   C
I believe this wave will bear my weight,
    D
So let it flow.

Chorus 1

    G
Oh sit down, oh sit down, oh sit down,
C   D
Sit down next to me.
   G
Sit down, down, down, down,
   C   D
Down in sympathy.

Instrumental ‖: G | G | C | D   :‖

Verse 2

```
              G                          C              D
Now I'm relieved to hear that you've been to some far out places.
              G                   C     D
It's hard to carry on when you feel all alone.
      G                            C                    D
Now I've swung back down again it's worse than it was before.
            G                     C              D
If I hadn't seen such riches I could live with being poor.
```

Chorus 2   As Chorus 1

Link | G | G | G | G ||

Middle

```
      G                                  (C)              (D)
Those who feel the breath of sadness, sit down next to me.
      G                                  (C)              (D)
Those who find they're touched by madness, sit down next to me.
      G                                  (C)              (D)
Those who find themselves ridiculous, sit down next to me.
          G
In love, in fear, in hate, in tears,
          C         D
In love, in fear, in hate, in tears,
          G
In love, in fear, in hate, in tears,
          C         D
In love, in fear, in hate.
G       | G      | C      | D      |
Down.
G       | G      | C      | D      ||
Down.
```

Chorus 3   As Chorus 1

Chorus 4

```
            G
Oh sit down, oh sit down, oh sit down,
C                  D
Sit down next to me.
        G
Sit down, down, down, down,
          C           D
Down in sympathy.
G
Down.
```

So Lonely

Words & Music by
Sting

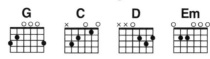

Verse 1

   G   D   Em   C
Well someone told me yesterday

   G   D   Em   C
That when you throw your love away

   G   D   Em   C
You act as if you just don't care,

   G   D   Em   C
You look as if you're going somewhere.

   G   D   Em   C
But I just can't convince myself,

   G   D   Em   C
I couldn't live with no-one else,

   G   D   Em   C
And I can only play that part

   G   D   Em   C
And sit and nurse my broken heart.

Chorus 1

   G   D   Em   C
So lonely,   so lonely,   so lonely,

   G   D   Em   C
So lonely,   so lonely,   so lonely,

   G   D   Em   C
So lonely,   so lonely,   so lonely,

   G   D   Em   C
So lonely,   so lonely,   so lonely.

<pre>
                    G   D   Em   C
Verse 2   Now no-one's knocked upon my door
                    G   D   Em   C
                               For a thousand years or more.
                    G   D   Em   C
                               All made up and nowhere to go,
                    G   D   Em   C
                               Welcome to this one man show.
                    G   D   Em   C
                               Just take a seat, they're always free,
                    G   D   Em   C
                               No surprise, no mystery.
                    G   D   Em   C
                               In this theatre that I call my soul,
                    G   D   Em   C
                               I always play the starring role.

                    G   D   Em   C
Chorus 2   So lonely, so lonely, so lonely,
                    G   D   Em   C
                               So lonely, so lonely, so lonely,
                    G   D   Em   C
                               So lonely, so lonely, so lonely,
                    G   D   Em   C
                               So lonely, so lonely, so lonely.
</pre>

Instrumental ‖: G | D | Em | C   :‖ *Play 7 times*

                | G | D | Em | C   ‖

                                           So lonely,

<pre>
                    G   D   Em   C
Outro   ‖: so lonely, so lonely, so lonely.   :‖ *Repeat to fade*
</pre>

Take It Easy

Words & Music by
Jackson Browne & Glenn Frey

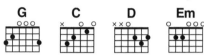

Intro
‖: G | G | C | D :‖ G | G ‖

Verse 1
        G
Well I'm a-runnin' down the road tryin' to loosen my load,
             D   **C**
I've got seven women on my mind.
G   **D**
Four that wanna own me, two that wanna stone me,
  C   **G**
One says she's a friend of mine.

Chorus 1
         Em   **C** **G**
Take it easy, take it ea - sy,
            C   **Em**
Don't let the sound of your own wheels drive you crazy.
       C   **G**   **C**   **G**
Lighten up while you still can, don't even try to understand,
       C   **G**
Just find a place to make your stand and take it easy.

| G | G ‖

Verse 2
        G
Well I'm a-standin' on a corner in Winslow, Arizona,
          D   **C**
And such a fine sight to see;
      G   **D**
It's a girl, my Lord, in a flat-bed Ford,
      C   **G**
Slowin' down to take a look at me.

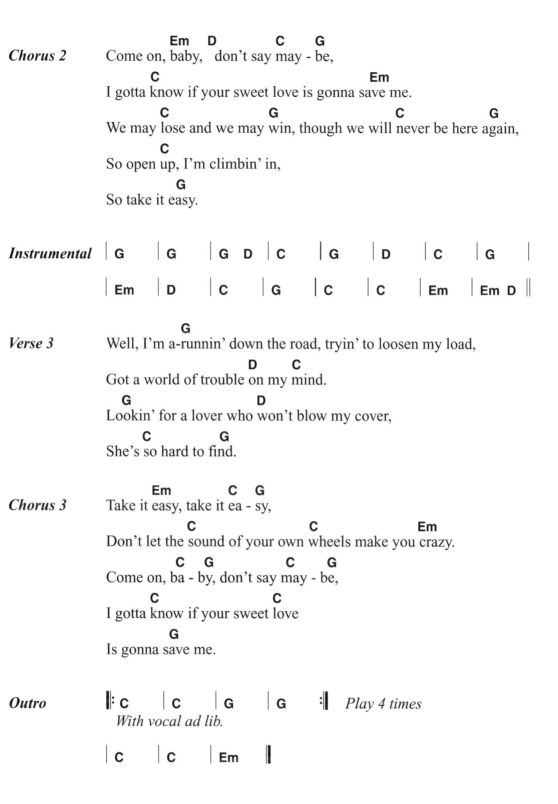

Chorus 2

          Em   D   **C**   **G**
Come on, baby,   don't say may - be,

        C   **Em**
I gotta know if your sweet love is gonna save me.

         C   **G**   **C**   **G**
We may lose and we may win, though we will never be here again,

         C
So open up, I'm climbin' in,

            G
So take it easy.

Instrumental | **G** | **G** | **G** **D** | **C** | **G** | **D** | **C** | **G** |

              | **Em** | **D** | **C** | **G** | **C** | **C** | **Em** | **Em** **D** ‖

Verse 3

            G
Well, I'm a-runnin' down the road, tryin' to loosen my load,

                    D   **C**
Got a world of trouble on my mind.

    G   **D**
Lookin' for a lover who won't blow my cover,

        C   **G**
She's so hard to find.

Chorus 3

          Em   **C** **G**
Take it easy, take it ea - sy,

                   C   **C**   **Em**
Don't let the sound of your own wheels make you crazy.

              C **G**   **C** **G**
Come on, ba - by, don't say may - be,

        C   **C**
I gotta know if your sweet love

          G
Is gonna save me.

Outro   ‖: **C** | **C** | **G** | **G** :‖   *Play 4 times*
             With vocal ad lib.

       | **C** | **C** | **Em** ‖

The Joker

Words & Music by
Steve Miller, Eddie Curtis & Ahmet Ertegun

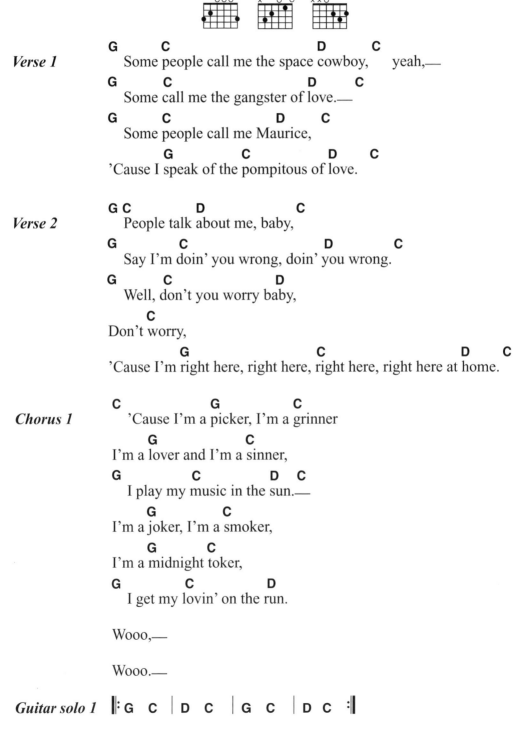

Verse 1

G   C   D   C
Some people call me the space cowboy,   yeah,—

G   C   D   C
Some call me the gangster of love.—

G   C   D   C
Some people call me Maurice,

          G   C   D   C
'Cause I speak of the pompitous of love.

Verse 2

G C   D   C
People talk about me, baby,

G   C   D   C
Say I'm doin' you wrong, doin' you wrong.

G   C   D
Well, don't you worry baby,

        C
Don't worry,

        G   C   D   C
'Cause I'm right here, right here, right here, right here at home.

Chorus 1

      C   G   C
'Cause I'm a picker, I'm a grinner

        G   C
I'm a lover and I'm a sinner,

G   C   D C
I play my music in the sun.—

        G   C
I'm a joker, I'm a smoker,

        G   C
I'm a midnight toker,

G   C   D
I get my lovin' on the run.

Wooo,—

Wooo.—

Guitar solo 1 ‖: G C | D C | G C | D C :‖

Verse 3

```
G                C          D       C
You're the cutest thing that I ever did see,
   G              C              D              C
I really love your peaches, want to shake your tree.
G          C                        D          C
    Lovey-dovey, lovey-dovey, lovey-dovey all the time,——
G          C              D                    C
    Ooo-weee baby, I'll sure show you a good time.
```

Chorus 2

```
      C            G          C
      'Cause I'm a picker, I'm a grinner,
         G              C
I'm a lover and I'm a sinner,
G          C          D   C
    I play my music in the sun.——
         G          C
I'm a joker, I'm a smoker,
      G          C
I'm a midnight toker,
G              C              D     C
    I sure don't want to hurt no-one.
```

Guitar solo 2

```
| G  C  | G  C  | G  C  | D  C  |

| G  C  | G  C  | G  C  | D    ||
```

Link

```
D
Wooo—


Wooo—
```

Verse 4

```
G    C              D          C
Peo - ple keep talking a - bout me baby,
G    C          D     C
    They say I'm doin' you wrong.
G    C                    D              C
    Well don't you worry, don't worry, no don't worry mama,
G          C          D     C
    'Cause I'm right here at home.
```

Verse 5   As Verse 3

Fade out

The Times They Are A-Changin

Words & Music by
Bob Dylan

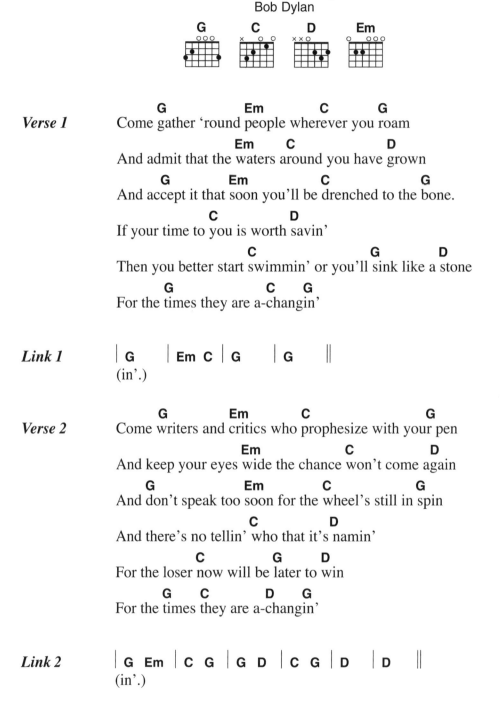

Verse 1

         G   **Em**   **C**   **G**
Come gather 'round people wherever you roam
                  Em   **C**   **D**
And admit that the waters around you have grown
         G   **Em**   **C**   **G**
And accept it that soon you'll be drenched to the bone.
            C   **D**
If your time to you is worth savin'
                   C   **G**   **D**
Then you better start swimmin' or you'll sink like a stone
         G   **C**   **G**
For the times they are a-changin'

Link 1

| G | Em C | G | G | ||
(in'.)

Verse 2

         G   **Em**   **C**   **G**
Come writers and critics who prophesize with your pen
                  Em   **C**   **D**
And keep your eyes wide the chance won't come again
         G   **Em**   **C**   **G**
And don't speak too soon for the wheel's still in spin
              C   **D**
And there's no tellin' who that it's namin'
             C   **G**   **D**
For the loser now will be later to win
         G   **C**   **D** **G**
For the times they are a-changin'

Link 2

| G Em | C G | G D | C G | D | D | ||
(in'.)

Verse 3

G   Em   C   G
Come senators, congressmen, please heed the call

                  Em   C   D
Don't stand in the doorway, don't block up the hall

  G   Em   C   G
For he that gets hurt will be he who has stalled

               C   D
There's a battle outside and it is ragin'.

                     C   G   D
Will soon shake your windows and rattle your walls

        G   C   D   G
For the times they are a-changin'.

Link 3

| G | D C | D G ‖
(in')

Verse 4

G   Em   C   G
Come mothers and fathers throughout the land

                 Em   C   D
And don't criticize what you can't understand

    G   Em   C   G
Your sons and your daughters are beyond your command

               C   D
Your old road is rapidly agin'.

                   C   G   D
Please get out of the new one if you can't lend your hand

        G   D   G
For the times they are a-changin'.

Link 4

| G | Em C | G | D C |
(in'.)

| G D | D G | C D | G | G   ‖

Verse 5

             Em   **C**   **G**
The line it is drawn the curse it is cast

                Em   **C**   **D**
The slow one now will later be fast

           G   **Em**   **C**   **G**
As the present now will later be past

              C   **D**
The order is rapidly fadin'.

                 C   **G**   **D**
And the first one now will later be last

           G   **Em**   **D** **G**
For the times they are a-changin'.

Coda | **G** | **Em C** | **G** | **Em C** ‖
           (in'.)

Two Princes

Words & Music by
Chris Barron, Eric Schenkman, Mark White & Aaron Comess

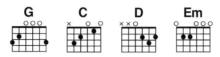

Intro   **1 bar drums**   ‖: **G Em** | **D C** | **G Em** | **D C** :‖

Verse 1

G   **Em**   **D**
One, two princes kneel before you,

       C
That's what I said, now.

G   **Em**   **D**
Princes, Princes, who adore you,

      C
Just go ahead, now.

G   **Em**   **D**
One has diamonds in his pocket

      C
And that's some bread now,

G   **Em**   **D**
This one said he wants to buy you rockets,

      C
Ain't in his head, now.

Link 1 | **G Em** | **D C** | **G Em** | **D C** |

Verse 2

G   **Em**   **D**
This one, he got a princely racket,

      C
That's what I said, now.

G   **Em**   **D**
Got some big seal upon his jacket,

     C
Ain't in his head, now.

      G   **Em**   **D**
You marry him, your father will condone you,

cont.

C
How 'bout that, now?

G   **Em**   **D**
You marry me, your father will disown you,

        C
He'll eat his hat, now.

Pre-chorus 1

C
Marry him or marry me,

G
I'm the one that loves you baby can't you see?

      C
I ain't got no future or a family tree,

  D
But I know what a prince and lover ought to be,

I know what a prince and lover ought to be.

Chorus 1

      G   **Em**   **D**
Said, if you want to call me baby,

    C
Just go ahead, now.

      G   **Em**   **D**
An' if you'd like to tell me maybe,

    C
Just go ahead, now.

      G   **Em**   **D**
And if you wanna buy me flowers

    C
Just go ahead, now.

      G   **Em**   **D**
And if you like to talk for hours

    C
Just go ahead, now.

Guitar Solo   ‖: G Em | D C | G Em | D C :| C | G | C | D | D | D

Verse 3   As Verse 1

Pre-chorus 2   As Pre-chorus 1

Chorus 2

          G   N.C.
Said, if you want to call me baby,

Just go ahead, now.

An' if you'd like to tell me maybe,

Just go ahead, now.

And if you wanna buy me flowers,

Just go ahead, now.

And if you like to talk for hours,

Just go ahead, now.

Chorus 3

          G   Em   D
Said, if you want to call me baby,
          C
Just go ahead, now.
          G   D
An' if you'd like to tell me maybe,
          C
Just go ahead, now.
          G   Em   D
And if you like to buy me flowers,
          C
Just go ahead, now.
          G   Em   D
And if you like to talk for hours
          C
Just go ahead, now.

Chorus 4   𝄆 As Chorus 1 𝄇   *Repeat to fade w/ad lib vocals*

Waterloo

Words & Music by
Benny Andersson, Stig Anderson & Björn Ulvaeus

| G | C | D | Em |

Intro | G | G | G | G ||

Verse 1
       G   D   C   D
My, my, at Waterloo Napoleon did surrender,
       G   D   C   D   Em
Oh yeah, and I have met my dest-i-ny in quite a similar way.

The history book on the shelf
Em   **D**
Is always repeating itself. _____

Chorus 1
 G   C
Waterloo, I was defeated, you won the war.
 D   G   D
Waterloo, promise to love you for evermore.
 G   C
Waterloo, couldn't escape if I wanted to.
 D   G
Waterloo, knowing my fate is to be with you.
                     D   G
Wa, Wa, Wa, Wa, Waterloo, finally facing my Waterloo.

| G | G | G ||

Verse 2
       G   D   C   D
My, my, I tried to hold you back but you were stronger,
       G   D   C   D   Em
Oh yeah, and now it seems my only   chance is givin' up the fight.

And how could I ever refuse?
Em   **D**
I feel like I win when I lose. _____

Chorus 2

     G   **C**
Waterloo, I was defeated, you won the war.

     D   **G**   **D**
Waterloo, promise to love you for evermore.

     G   **C**
Waterloo, couldn't escape if I wanted to.

     D   **G**
Waterloo, knowing my fate is to be with you.

                    D   **G**
Wa, Wa, Wa, Wa, Waterloo, finally facing my Waterloo.

Link

            Em
So how could I ever refuse?

                 D
I feel like I win when I lose.

Outro

     G   **C**
Waterloo, couldn't escape if I wanted to.

     D   **G**
Waterloo, knowing my fate is to be with you.

                    D   **G**
‖: Wa, Wa, Wa, Wa, Waterloo, finally facing my Waterloo.

                  D
Wa, Wa, Wa, Wa, Waterloo,

                    G
Knowing my fate is to be with you. :‖ *Repeat to fade*

Wonderful Tonight

Words & Music by
Eric Clapton

(2 bar count in)

Intro   ‖: G | D | C | D   :‖

Verse 1
```
G                D
It's late in the evening,
C                        D
She's wondering what clothes to wear.
G                D
She puts on her make-up,
C                D
And brushes her long blonde hair.
C                D
And then she asks me,
G        D     Em
"Do I look alright?"
            C            D            (G)
And I say, "Yes, you look wonderful tonight."
```

Link | G | D | C | D   ‖
(-night.)

Verse 2
```
G                D
We go to a party
C                        D
And everyone turns to see
G                D
This beautiful lady
C                        D
That's walking around with me.
C                D
And then she asks me,
G        D     Em
"Do you feel alright?"
            C        D        G
And I say, "Yes, I feel wonderful tonight."
```

Bridge

        C   D
I feel wonderful because I see
         G   D   Em
The love-light in your eyes,
           C   D
And the wonder of it all
            C   D   (G)
Is that you just don't realise how much I love you.

Link   ‖: G | D | C | D   :‖
         (love you.)

Verse 3

    G   D
  It's time to go home now
  C   D
  And I've got an aching head,
  G   D
  So I give her the car keys,
  C   D
  She helps me to bed.
  C   D
  And then I tell her
  G   D   Em
  As I turn out the light,
            C   D   G   D Em D
I say, "My darling, you were wonderful tonight.
          C   D   (G)
Oh, my darling, you were wonderful tonight."

Coda   ‖: G | D | C | D   :‖ G   ‖
         (-night.)

Yellow Submarine

Words & Music by
John Lennon & Paul McCartney

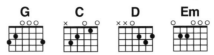

Verse 1

      D   C   G
In the town where I was born,

Em   C   D
Lived a man who sailed to sea,

G   D   C   G
And he told us of his life,

Em   C   D
In the land of submarines.

Verse 2

G   D   C   G
So we sailed up to the sun,

Em   C   D
Till we found the sea of green,

G   D   C   G
And we lived beneath the waves,

Em   C   D
In our yellow submarine.

Chorus 1

G   D
We all live in a yellow submarine,

                   G
Yellow submarine, yellow submarine.

              D
We all live in a yellow submarine,

                   G
Yellow submarine, yellow submarine.

Verse 3

(G)   D   C G
And our friends are all aboard,

Em   C   D
Many more of them live next door,

G   D   C   G   D
And the band begins to play.

Link | G   G | D   G ‖

Chorus 2

G   D
We all live in a yellow submarine,
                G
Yellow submarine, yellow submarine.
            D
We all live in a yellow submarine,
                G
Yellow submarine, yellow submarine.

Instrumental | D   C | G   Em | C | D   G |

                     | D   C | G   Em | C | D   G ‖

Verse 4

(G) D   C   G
As we live a life of ease,
Em   C   D
Every one of us has all we need,
G   D   C   G
Sky of blue and sea of green,
Em   C   D
In our yellow submarine.

Chorus 3

G   D
We all live in a yellow submarine,
                G
Yellow submarine, yellow submarine.
            D
‖: We all live in a yellow submarine,
                G
Yellow submarine, yellow submarine. :‖ *Repeat to fade*

Sweet Home Alabama

Words & Music by
Ronnie Van Zant, Ed King & Gary Rossington

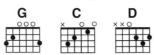

Intro
x4
‖: D   C | G   :‖

Verse 1
D   C   G
Big wheels keep on turning
D   C   G
Carry me home to see my kin
D   C   G
Singing songs about the Southland
D   C   G
I miss Alabama once again

And I think its a sin, yes.

Link
x2
‖: D   C | G   :‖

Verse 2
D   C   G
Well I heard mister Young sing about her,
D   C   G
Well, I heard ole Neil put her down
D   C   G
Well, I hope Neil Young will remember
D   C   G
A Southern man don't need him around anyhow.

Chorus 1
D   C   G   C
Sweet home Alabama
D   C   G   C
Where the skies are so blue,
D   C   G   C
Sweet Home Alabama
D   C   G   C
Lord, I'm coming home to you.

x2

Instrumental ‖: D C | G :‖

Verse 3

    D   C   G   C
In Birmingham they love the gov'nor, (ooh, ooh, ooh)

    D   C   G
Now we all did what we could do

    D   C   G
Now Watergate does not bother me

    D   C   G
Does your conscience bother you?

Tell the truth.

Chorus 2

    D   C   G   C
Sweet home Alabama

    D   C   G   C
Where the skies are so blue

    D   C   G   C
Sweet Home Alabama

    D   C   G
Lord, I'm coming home to you

Here I come, Alabama.

x10

Instrumental ‖: D C | G :‖

Verse 4

    D   C   G
Now Muscle Shoals has got the Swampers

    D   C   G
And they've been known to pick a song or two (yes they do),

    D   C   G
Lord they get me off so much

    D   C   G
They pick me up when I'm feeling blue

Now how about you?

Chorus 3

D   C   G   C
Sweet home Alabama

D   C   G   C
Where the skies are so blue

D   C   G   C
Sweet Home Alabama

D   C   G F C
Lord, I'm coming home to you.

Chorus 4

D   C   G   C
Sweet home Alabama (oh sweet home baby)

D   C   G   C
Where the skies are so blue (and the guv'nor's true)

D   C   G   C
Sweet Home Alabama (Lordy)

D   C   G
Lord, I'm coming home to you.

Outro   ‖: D C | G :‖ *Repeat to fade*

Yeah, yeah Montgomery's got the answer.